Be

HOMOEOPATHIC
TREATMENT FOR BIRDS

SAFFRON WALDEN
THE C. W. DANIEL COMPANY LTD

First published in Great Britain
by The C. W. Daniel Company Ltd
1 Church Path, Saffron Walden
Essex CB10 1JP, England

© Beryl M. Chapman 1991

ISBN 0 85207 235 X

Set in 11pt Melliza by MS Typesetting,
Castle Camps, Cambridge and
Printed by Hillman Printers, Frome,
Somerset, England

CONTENTS

FOREWORD

It is interesting that a number of patients who have come to me with a chronic condition have gone to their G.P. when something like 'flu' has developed. When I showed surprise and asked why, I was always told the same thing — 'I didn't know you treated 'flu' '.

I am sure it will stretch the imagination of many people to realise that birds, large and small, can also derive great benefit from homoeopathy.

I congratulate Beryl on the work she has done — treating nearly two thousand birds in a year is no mean feat, and she has had to work very hard since the early days when I remember her caring for a few 'strays' in a less than large garden.

Anybody who is interested in the welfare of birds, and we hear of more and more people who are conscious that birds do need help and care at times, will learn a great deal from this little book. Beryl gives a long list of diseases and things that can damage birds (I had no idea there were so many!) with the

1

appropriate homoeopathic remedies and dosage.

The case histories make very interesting reading and I feel sure that many more people will be encouraged to do all they can for birds after reading them.

I have helped many birds with Arnica which can bring a little feathered-friend back to life after being knocked unconscious by flying into a brick wall or building and this is fascinating to watch.

We have books on homoeopathic treatment for human beings and animals and it is very exciting now to have this one on the treatment of birds.

Phyllis Speight

INTRODUCTION

It is the sickening thump as a bird flies into the window-pane and falls senseless to the ground that sends us hurrying out to pick it up.

The first question of the average person is — 'Is it still alive?' Having verified that it is, then the next question is, 'What am I to do with it? Do I kill it to stop it from suffering, or can I save its life?'

This book is aimed at helping the little casualities that somehow or other land up in our hands. Whether you have aviaries full of exotics, a pet budgerigar, are part of a wild bird rescue team or just a lover of free wild birds in the garden; the contents of this book are written so that you can understand how to help injured birds homoeopathically. Homoeopathy has been available to humans for a long time, to animals fairly recently, but treatment for birds by only a few practitioners. Having worked amongst injured wild birds for approximately fifteen years and a user of these remedies, I have adapted them accordingly and compiled this work to help others.

One of the chief killers of birds is shock and fear and this is where homoepathic remedies are excellent. Usually I treat a new bird for shock first, before going on to what is really wrong, otherwise, instead of a bird dying from an infected wound, it dies quickly from shock before you have had time to treat the infection.

You will find that this book is arranged in alphabetical order of diseases, for quick and easy references. Sometimes case histories are added in the appropriate sections.

As homoeopathic remedies treat the whole bird, animal or person, it is in fact the sufferer's reaction to disease that determines the choice of remedy. That is why I say things like, 'If the bird is agitated and frightened give so-and-so and if the bird is calm, cool and quiet give something else'. I have explored the reasons for this in the chapter 'Homoeopathy and how it works'.

Apart from the right remedy, an important thing for a bird (even one that knows you) is quiet, warmth and in most cases to be left alone between treatments. Most like a small, dark box as they feel secure and safe and so can sleep. The exception, of course, is your own cage bird which would prefer its own cage. Medication, sleep, relaxation and warmth are the main healers. The only break in that rule is to remember that small birds cannot go long without food. To eat they must have light, and they must also feel well enough to want to eat. This is the part that must be left to the individual who is trying to help an injured creature.

'Creature', because, although I have written this book primarily for birds, if an injured hedgehog turns up on your doorstop, you can look up the injury page and treat the little chap accordingly. Your biggest problem is persuading him to uncurl!

HOMOEOPATHY AND HOW IT WORKS

In the days of Dr. Samuel Hahnemann, who rediscovered homoeopathic remedies in the 1790's, medical substances were proved by healthy men and women. This was to find out what effects a material dose had on a person, because conversely, if a sick person portrayed similar symptoms it was found that a potentied dose of the same material would cure the patient. The findings of Dr. Hahnemann are still the same today, except that more and more remedies have been discovered. There are, in fact, now approximately 3,000 different substances in varying potencies.

Let us take as an example, Belladonna, the familiar Deadly Nightshade found in our hedgerows. This plant is, as its name implies, deadly; and if eaten attacks the nervous system causing twitching, convulsions, pain, hot red skin, flushed face and glaring eyes. If, however, a patient shows these symptoms, or some of them, the chances are a potentied dose or so will cure them.

6

Likewise, if a patient has swelling of the skin with redness and pain, symptoms resembling a bee sting, then a potentised medicine made from the honey bee called Apis would be administered. Like cures like — the main principle of homoeopathy.

Homoeopathy cures the whole person, not just a part — such as stomach-ache. The stomach-ache is caused by something and the something must be found. The patient's reaction to the something, then, tells the homoeopath what medicine to give, to cure the stomach-ache.

If six people catch the 'flu' from the same source, each can react differently, as they are susceptible in different ways. Some may have severe sore throats, some may have streaming noses, others ache with or without headaches, some can even die whilst others barely show any severe symptoms at all. It stands to reason, therefore, that each person has a remedy personal to their own reaction to the 'flu'. In homoeopathy, a name of an illness is not important as it is the body that tells us how it can be cured. This way we cure the whole person.

In standard medicine, too often symptoms are repressed and not cured, and then develop into something more serious. If we take an example of Eczema, if it is repressed by ointments, it is reputed to come out in later years as Asthma. If it is not cured at this point, it can return as a form of heart trouble. Once again in different people, different diseases occur. the energy of homoeopathic remedies help the body to cure itself by eliminating symptoms from the centre to the circumference.

With birds or animals, the same system applies. A group of seagulls suffering from the effects of food poisoning, after taking bad food from rubbish dumps, respond to different remedies. As they themselves display different symptoms, their bodies react in different ways. A bird may be quiet, anxious and snappy, or aggressive and snappy. It may have a weak peck or a strong peck; it may be cold or warm; or salivating; all these are guides to the correct remedy.

POTENCY AND DOSE

Mystery seems to surround how homoeopathic remedies work. Why they are gentle to use, and with no side effects. I will explain a little of how they are made, as this is important in understanding them, apart from being interesting.

The pharmacist starts with the substance in its raw state and proceeds to make it into a liquid which is called the mother tincture. One drop of this is added to 100 drops of alcohol and is then shaken concussively to make the first potency. The second is made by taking one drop of the first potency and adding it to another 100 drops of alcohol and again shaken concussively. By the time the third potency is reached it is one part to 1,000,000. There is not much left of the original substance. Try to imagine how little of the substance is in potencies 12, 30, 200 and upwards. The higher the potency, the more dynamic is the action and these high potencies are not recommended for use by the inexperienced, unless prescribed by a homoeopathic practitioner. It is a form of energy that does the work, and can react extremely quickly if correctly given. The lower potencies — up to 30 can be safely used as described in the following pages, even the occasional 200, if administered as prescribed.

It is not the quantity taken as in orthodox medicine but the repetition, therefore one dose in tablet, pill or powder form, is correct for a sparrow or a swan, and similarly, an animal or a human-being.

As we are handling an energy and not a substance, it is easily dissipated by touch or even smell (good or bad). Therefore, do not handle tablets and replace them in the container, but tip one onto a clean teaspoon and close the lid immediately. Place the tablet into a clean mouth or beak i.e. one with no signs of recent food intake. About fifteen minutes before and after a dose of medicine it is best to abstain from food. Sniff the air before opening the container to make sure it is free of smells to safeguard the stock.

Frequency of dose varies with the urgency of treatment. You can give 3 or 4 doses half an hour apart for bad cases, but always stop when improvement shows and thereafter monitor doses to be dispensed when required. Too much repetition can hamper improvement. Very often 3 or 4 doses is enough and you will find that the symptoms have changed, therefore you must change remedies to match the symptoms.

Do not let all this put you off as detailed instructions will be found in the main alphabetical section on diseases. Potency can be varied: if you have a remedy in 6 and I advise 30, then use 6 but you will need more, and more frequent dosing. For birds, the least handling the better, therefore I stick to higher potencies. However, do not use 200 unless I have stated it, as it is not always safe to do so. Nonetheless, ailments requiring a fast action then 200 is the one, and for nerve problems especially the spine.

In some remedies I have mentioned the duration of action on the patient. Not all remedies have a known working time. From this it is easy to understand why so few doses are required, as it remains in the system and keeps working.

It will be noticed that many remedies overlap in use. However, careful study will reveal their differences. Where I have shown a semi-colon, the bird does not have to have all the symptoms, but a comma, shows a qualification.

It is impossible in a work this size to show much detail, but I hope I have given you enough for some useful healing.

Homoeopathic remedies are gentle

and yet fast in their action. When used correctly and to completion it renders a complaint null and void. Because antibiotic treatment not only kills the bacteria which is causing the trouble but also destroys friendly bacteria that live in the body and fight infection, the patient is left defenceless for a time. Homoeopathic remedies find the weakness in the body and strengthen it to fight disease.

For awkward beaks a clean pair of pointed tweezers is very helpful in inserting a tablet to the back of the throat or part of a tablet if the beak has a small opening.

SYMPTOMS AND REMEDIES

This main section is made up of remedies that I have used many times with success. Every case, however, is different. You will notice in some of the case histories I have deviated a little from my initial suggested medication because I have had to follow the symptoms. A further explanation will be found in the Bird Materia Medica section.

I mention from time to time, Hypercal, which can be obtained as a cream, ointment or tincture. I like to stock the cream and the tincture, because the cream is soft and easy to apply, especially to parts that you want to keep dry. The diluted tincture (not neat because the pure alcohol used in its formation will sting) is good for nasty wounds that you do not want to touch, or others where a wet treatment is better.

Remember to stop or reduce dosage as soon as improvement occurs. Do not feel that, like standard medicine, that you must finish a set course. A small amount works far better, and in most cases, if

13

you get no reaction within two or three doses, then you have chosen the wrong remedy, so look again for an alternative.

Where several different remedies are needed, the order of severity is of importance. It's no good treating a broken leg if the patient is going to die very soon of shock.

ABSCESS Only occasionally do birds get abscesses and when they do it is mostly due to infection from a wound.

— Where there is redness, pain and throbbing but not much swelling use *Belladonna 30* — 1 dose every 2 hours (approx.) till improvement occurs.

— Where there is much swelling with or without the other symptoms use *Apis 6* and dose as above.

— If neither of these has checked the inflammation then use *Merc Sol 6* — dose as above.

— If matter has formed, then use *Hepar Sulph 6* and dose approximately 3 hours apart.

ANTIDOTE TO ANAESTHETIC VAPOURS If a bird is slow coming round from an anaesthetic after surgery then use *Acetic Acid 6* at 15-minute intervals till the bird is conscious. However only resort to this if you feel recovery is definitely too slow because its administration limits further quick use of other remedies, as it antidotes some of them too. It antidotes Aconite — Hepar Sulph — Ignatia — Opium. As Aconite in turn antidotes Acetic Acid, then a dose or two of Aconite afterwards will nullify any further action and enable you to continue further treatment as required. The problem, of course, is the delay.

Case History A black-headed gull had a badly broken wing and the skin was torn and ragged. The bird had to be anaesthetised so the bone could be replaced under the skin and the lacerations stitched up. There was a fair amount of blood loss and the patient therefore weak and very slow to come round, so she was given Acetic Acid 6, two doses, fifteen minutes apart. She came round and was standing on her feet twenty minutes after the administration of the first dose.

BEREAVEMENT Some types of bird will mate for life if possible, and are greatly upset if they lose their mates. There are exceptions, where one is not loyal and flies off to find another mate, but that is another story! Swans can suffer very much if a mate dies, and the remaining one often just sits around waiting. The danger is that they can give up the desire to eat and slowly fade away. The remedy is *Ignatia 200* — one dose a day for several days, but no more than a week. I prefer to drop the potency to 30 if there is any reason to continue dosing. If the bird is not eating by this stage, then I resort to annoying the patient, to get a positive reaction. I do this by repeatedly throwing some moist food onto their backs. They grab it and toss it away. If this is continued they not only get the taste of food, by picking it up, but their annoyance brings them out of their listlessness.

Case History A cob or male swan, had tragically witnessed the death of his mate and was found several days later, still sitting by her body. He did not resist being picked up except for a miserable hiss. He was taken to the sanctuary and placed in a warm room with other swans, but he refused to eat. He was given Ignatia 200 each day for three days, and during that time I kept making a nuisance of myself to him by throwing a handful of moist Vitalyn dog food onto his snowy white back. He hissed his annoyance and grabbed beaksful of it to throw away, but each time he began to get a taste for it. By the end of the third day he had joined the others with his beak in the bowl of food. He did not actually stand up for another two days as the shock of his bereavement had weakened him. It would have been useless to take him back to his lake as the memory would have upset him again, so he was kept with others, until he found a new 'lady friend', a young pen who had just got her adult colour in her bill. When they became firm friends they were taken to his old lake and released together. Fortunately the lake had not been taken over by another pair of swans.

BLEEDING This is covered more specifically in other sections e.g. Injuries but a general guide is set out here. Usually the use of *Hypercal* is sufficient to stop bleeding and commence good healing, however, sometimes haemorrhage occurs where we must act quickly.

— For open, painful wounds, with weakness from loss of blood, also after operations, use *Hamamelis 30* for 3 or 4 doses (½ hour to 1 hour apart as necessary).

— A weak bird with sepsis and/or skin a dark purple colour use *Lachesis 30* and dose as above.

— An excellent healer to deep tissue after surgery is *Bellis Perennis 30* — dose 3 or 4 times over a couple of days.

Case History A moorhen flew low over a road straight into a moving car. Fortunately, the driver stopped and picked up the practically unconscious bird. When he arrived, he was bleeding from his beak, his eyes were shut and his limbs, head and neck hung as though he were dead. He was fighting for breath through the blood. Death can soon follow this sort of situation. I held him head down with the tip of his beak just touching water, which if done with care can draw the blood from the mouth. As soon as I was able, I turned him right way up and gave him a *Calendula 30* which stopped further bleeding very quickly. This time I gave the *Aconite 30* for shock in the second instance, because the main urgency was to stop the bleeding. Because his injury was from a blow, I was afraid of possible concussion, so I followed the Aconite with two doses of *Arnica*, 2 hours apart. The bird flew away a week later.

BLOWS Arnica is marvellous for alleviating shock after a blow and also helps to reduce the pain, swelling and bruising. As birds are quick to die from shock, *Arnica 30* 3 or 4 times in the day (or shorter time duration — if urgently needed) can make all the difference from winning or losing the patient.

— If the bone has been bruised, then follow the Arnica the following day with *Ruta 6* or *30*, twice a day for up to a week if needed.

— Sometimes the joint is stiff, maybe after suspected bruising, then *Calc carb 30* is good for 2 or 3 doses.

Case History A cock sparrow was found by the road-side, his leg semi-paralysed. Presuming he was hit by a car on the base of his spine, he was given *Arnica 30* and after three doses, two hours apart, he began to move this leg. He was standing up the following morning and was given another Arnica. He flew off the next day.

BROKEN BONES This causes shock, fear, pain and if not treated quickly, infection and/or swelling soon follows.

Firstly we must treat for shock, and we have two choices open to us. [If the bird is hot and agitated and there are skin lacerations, I give Aconite 200 for one dose.]

— If the skin is intact and the bird calm, then I give Arnica 200 for one dose.

The next stage is to set the broken bones, which is usually a vet's job. If for some reason it must be a 'do-it-yourself job' then use something for a splint. If a wing bone is broken, bind the wing in a closed position, aligning the broken bone and using the good bone next to it as a splint. Masking tape is excellent as it holds very well and can be taken off easily with scissors. I do not like sticking plaster as it can do too much damage in its removal. Do not bind the wing to the body unless you have no choice as birds usually react badly to this, either falling over, or finding it difficult to breathe or refusing to eat because their crop feels restricted. Another problem is the wing remaining stiff afterwards.

— If a leg bone is broken, then a feather quill serves very well as a splint and can be bound with masking tape, the broken ends together.

— The healing time varies with the bone size and the muscle power. On average, a leg takes two weeks and a wing three weeks. A small bird will heal quicker than a big bird.

— Give *Symphytum 30* for about a quarter of the healing time, twice a day. This will speed up healing and give a strong, healthy join. It also helps to relieve pain during and after healing.

— Stiff limbs sometimes result from a break but frequently clear within days or a few weeks. Further medication for this can be found under section called Wings.

Case Histories A collared dove had the upper bone of its wing broken and a little hole punctured the skin where the bone was protruding.

The bird was very calm and quiet so he was given Arnica 30 to stop bruising and the bone was pulled back into the right place. Using masking tape the bone was bound to the lower part of the wing to use it as a splint, and one more piece of tape to lift the drooping lower edge as it was weak but not broken. Hypercal tincture was dripped into the hole made by the bone. The bird was standing within the hour and feeding by the end of the day. He had a course of Symphytum 30 twice a day for 5 days and after three weeks the binding was carefully removed and the bones felt. It was a good mend but the wing was stiff as the muscles had been strained. However, after a few weeks in an aviary where he could get about by walking up branches, he soon had his wing moving as he practised floating down from his perch. It was about two months before he could lift off and fly upwards, and then he was released.

A mallard drake had a broken leg. It was set using the flat section of a swan's quill as a splint. Symphytum was given daily for four days and after two weeks the binding was removed. The leg had repaired so well it was difficult to realise it had been broken.

A little owl was hit by a passing car and found lying with his legs sticking out behind him. One was badly strained and the other was broken. His first treatment was Arnica for pain and shock and to relieve bruising. Then his leg was set using part of a feather quill. He could not stand up because of the strained leg which he was unable to move. He was laid down on his front, but slightly elevated, so he could move his head and feed from a little bowl placed near his beak. He was given Symphytum in the morning and Ruta 30 in the evening for the strained leg. Normally only one medication is given at a time so we can monitor the reaction to it. In this case the Symphytum was a timed course for the bone, and if we had waited, the delay could have been damaging to the strained leg, causing it to remain stiff or useless.

By the time the binding had been taken off the broken leg, the little owl was able to stand, putting a bit of his weight on the strained leg. After a few weeks he was as good as new and released.

CHILLS It is usually during wet weather that birds get a chill especially when for some reason their plumage has lost its waterproofing, allowing water to penetrate their skin.

The symptoms are a fluffed-out appearance denoting that they are cold, usually with their heads under their wings or pulled down low to their bodies. Eyes are often closed, or have a lifeless, dejected expression. Sometimes they are watery. If the chill has gone down to the chest, they will be wheezing.

— If the bird is wet or it is wet weather the first choice would be *Dulcamara 30*. Dose the bird 2 or 3 times a day for approximately 3 days, depending on its reaction.

— If the bird is shivery and cold, with its right foot warm and its left foot cold then use *Lycopodium 30* and dose as above.

— If the weather is cold, dry and windy and particularly if the bird is hot and restless then the choice would be *Aconite 30* and dose as before.

— If the bird is cold, restless and anxious and the weather is changeable, then I would choose *Arsenicum 30*.

— If the bird is very tired, without fear but still fluffed-up and looking ill, I would give it *Gelsemium 30*.

Case Histories A peahen was found in rainy weather just sitting, with her head tucked under her wing. She was very drowsy and thin and had no strength to stand. She was put in a warm, dry place and given Dulcamara 30 twice a day for three days. This was all she needed to put her on her feet and feeding, although it was a couple of weeks before her weight returned.

An adult-sized cygnet was found in wet, cold conditions. She could not stand, was shivering and had wet nostrils. All she wanted was to be left alone to sleep. On examination, I found she had one hot foot and one cold foot, so she was treated with Lycopodium 30. Over the next couple of days she began to improve and was standing and eating by the end of the fourth day.

A chaffinch came in with a face wet from running eyes. The weather was cold and windy one day, and mild and wet the next, so the remedy choice was Arsenicum, especially as the bird was nervous and restless, in spite of having little strength. It took only two doses to get him settled and eating. The next day his face was dry and the following day he flew away.

COLLAPSE Sometimes we have to deal with the urgent situation of a bird that has collapsed. There is one remedy in homoeopathy that is known affectionately as the 'Corpse reviver'. Always have this on hand. As you must have a fast response it has to be *Carbo Veg 200* the 30 would not be quick enough.

— If the bird is cold and barely breathing, or gasping weakly, unable even to hold up its head — give *Carbo Veg 200*, 1 dose every ½ hour until improvement sets in.

— When the bird can open its eyes and hold up its head then change to Sulphur 200 for up to 3 doses, 3 hours apart.

— If further medication is required

then reduce the potency of Sulphur and Carbo Veg and continue to dose one of each alternatively for up to 3 days, 5 hours apart.

— Occasionally a bird is desperately taking short, gasping, breaths, but not wheezing, particularly if its legs are abnormally mottled, here *Oxalic Acid 12*, given every 15 minutes for 2 to 5 doses, can work wonders.

— If the bird is lacking energy after the first treatment then a few doses of *Gelsemium 30* should improve matters.

— If a herring gull, a lesser or great black-backed gull is unable to stand, wings and head hanging, and gasping for air, sometimes wheezing, also hot and salivating, a good remedy is *Ipecacuanha 30*. Dose 1 every hour for several doses.

Case Histories One hot summer within a period of ten days, over 40 gulls came to the sanctuary and after treatment all but one were able to fly away; some within 2 or 3 days, some by the end of 2 or 3 weeks, and some of the bigger ones taking longer.

Two herring gulls, both female, arrived in a state of collapse. Both were very hot, with their wings and legs quite loose and floppy as though without any bones. They were each settled in a box, side by side, and given Ipecacuanha. There was only time for three doses before bedtime. Next morning both were still alive, one improved and looking around, although through bleary eyes. The other one supporting her head on the tip of her bill, eyes shut. I changed to Arnica 30 for the improved one as this continues well after Ipec. in these circumstances. The other gull seemed to be breathing its last. Quickly I gave her Opium 30 and after this she held up her head. After one more dose I changed to Nat Mur 30 and I was delighted that she opened her eyes and tried to peck my hand. After several doses of Nat Mur the gull had progressed in as much as she was breathing comfortably, could hold up her head and keep her eyes open, but she was paralysed from the shoulders down. I gave her Gelsemium 30 which finally brought life into her limbs. It took several doses over a couple of days, but she stood and later was able to go outside with the others. Here you can see two birds with apparently the same symptoms but the disorder took differ-ent turns, so much so that one nearly died.

A black-headed gull had been found in a field unable to stand. The farmer had been dressing the seed so it was a suspected case of poisoning, possibly mercury. The gull was very sick, eyes nearly closed and having difficulty in breathing. He was able to stand shakily but kept falling over, in fact he seemed reluctant to lie down. Alumen should have been used but I did not have it at the time, so I gave Hepar Sulph 30, 3 times in the one day. By evening he was much improved and by the following morning he looked a different bird. He ate several sprats and flew off two days later.

CONCUSSION A sign of concussion in birds is detected if one is standing with its head hanging down between its legs, often with its head twisted to one side. It could also be lying down, often with wings extended and again with its head twisted or held sharply down against its neck. Sometimes the bird is flapping as though trying to fly, but its eyes are closed and its head and neck as just mentioned. In this latter case the bird often flutters round in circles dragging its legs behind it.

— Concussion is usually caused by flying into window-panes or into moving cars. Sometimes light-weight sea birds can be blown into buildings in a strong wind.

— The first remedy is *Arnica 200*, 3 or 4 doses, 1 hour apart. You can carry on with Arnica 30 if necessary afterwards, but an early start with 200 helps to avoid swelling of the head, and its consequential pain. Obviously a bird cannot eat in this state so must be helped as quickly as possible. If you have to carry on the medication with the 30 potency then reduce dosage to 4 doses a day.

— If the spine is injured and paralysis has set in, follow the 200 Arnica with Hypericum 200 with 2 to 3 doses, 2 hours apart. This is also a powerful pain killer if the problem is nerve injury. After this you could continue with Hypericum 30 for a few days.

— If paralysis persists after this treatment see section on Paralysis.

Case History Kestrel female. She was flying fast across a field and swooped low over a road and straight into an oncoming car. She tried to swerve away, so caught the blow on her lower spine. She had total downwards paralysis of the hips and great weakness in the shoulders. She lay on her front, a beautiful but helpless creature, her black eyes staring fearfully and in bewilderment.

First she was given Arnica 200 and then Hypericum 200. It was four days before she could push herself up by her wings. She had to be hand fed with small pieces of meat; a whole (dead) day-old chick went down her in a day.

She was getting fitter but her legs did not improve at all and remained sticking out behind her quite uselessly. The nerves had obviously been badly in-

28

jured. Ignatia 200 was then given once a day for one week, and then once every four days for another 5 doses. Gradually her legs began to move, and finally she got to her feet; legs spread widely for support, but she was up. After this she had no more medication as leg use was of the most importance, and the earlier medications would still be having some effect. See Materia Medica for working times.

You may note that I say in my treatment text, do this or that for only one or two days, and above you have just read Ignatia 200 for one week. I prefer to err on less rather than more as it's safer that way, however, if you have a case like the one above there is no reason why you cannot follow the same procedure, but space out the doses in the same way.

An adult sized cygnet flew into some overhead power-lines and crashed down to the field below, twisting a leg on landing. He burnt his neck feathers but did not burn his flesh, neither did he break any bones. He was very nervous and very aggressive. He was firstly given one Arnica 200 for shock from trauma, and then had one dose a day for two more days. The potency was then dropped to 30 and the Arnica continued for one week, still at one per day. The twisted leg gradually returned to normal position, and the cygnet was able to hobble on it. The web, however, remained closed as his toes were still affected. I then gave him Gelsemium 30, one a day for another week and watched as the web began to move as the toes regained mobility. By this time the cygnet was stamping around his room hissing at anyone he saw. He was a typical juvenile telling the world what a grand chap he was. He was carried outside to join other youngsters, and after a time he became inseparable from a young pen, and the two eventually went off to a private lake. Wings were intact, I must add, so it was up to the birds whether they stayed or left.

DIARRHOEA Birds are prone to diarrhoea, often from the shock of an injury, or an accident or just being caught or handled and caged. At other times it is due to an infection, starvation, or from poisoned foods. After surgery they sometimes have a bloody diarrhoea.

— If it is caused by starvation it is often bright green and liquid. Here *Arsenicum 30* for 3 or 4 doses over a couple of days can clear it up.

— If it is dark or light brown, and the condition does not clear in a day or two then *Alum 30* can be given, doses as above.

— After surgery *Arnica 200* for two doses — 2 hours apart, should correct any bloody diarrhoea and also aid healing and counter bruising, so it does a multi-job.

— If the weather is wet and the bird has a chill and diarrhoea, then *Dulcamara 30* will help.

— For diarrhoea caused by emotion, *Argentum Nit 30* can be helpful.

Case History A swan cob arrived and was very aggressive and nervous, he could stand but with difficulty. His left leg kept sliding away from him sideways. He had a very liquid diarrhoea but apart from the leg there did not seem to be anything wrong with him. The treatment therefore had to be for diarrhoea caused by shock. Presumably the swan had had an accident resulting in a sprained upper leg causing weakness there. As he was aggressive it was obviously affecting him emotionally, so he was given Argentum Nit 30 twice a day for two days. On the third day he was walking and his diarrhoea had cleared up. The Argentum Nit was chosen because it would not only remedy the diarrhoea in those circumstances, but it was ideal for lack of balance and withered legs. This particular swan did not have a withered leg but the leg was weak with no obvious injury.

FEET A bird can get a type of paralysis in the toes, when the toes droop and the bird cannot open them. They are soft and floppy so can be walked on with the toes curled underneath. Two or three days on Plumbum 6 at the rate of 3 times a day can correct this condition.

Case History A mallard duck arrived with a leg tucked under her feathers, webbed-foot closed and held limply. It was obviously painful so the bird was treated as for a blow and given *Arnica 30* for three doses over two days followed by *Ruta 6* for four days at the rate of 2 per day. At the end of this treatment the duck was walking about quite happily.

FLUID LOSS When a bird has been bleeding profusely and is consequently weak then *Phosphoric acid 30* can be given, 1 dose every 2 hours for 4 or 5 doses.
— If the weakness is from diarrhoea then *Carbo Veg 30* should be given instead.

INFECTION There are times, for example after surgery, when there is a danger of infection. Using standard medicine the preferred choice would be Penbritin as birds seem to react well to this. However, homoeopaths do not like to use an antibiotic because, not only does it kill the bacteria that it is supposed to kill, but other useful bacteria in the body as well, leaving the body temporarily susceptible to other infections after the Penbritin has worn off. You may have heard of people who have had 'flu' jabs say they did not have 'flu' that year but the following year without having jabs, they became more susceptible to 'flu'.

— The homoeopathic answer is *Hypericum 30 or 200*. The 30 being used as a preventive and the 200 for an emergency, or where a fast action is needed. It is even reputed to be effective in preventing tetanus, though I have had no experience of this myself.

— After surgery *Bellis Perennis 30* is excellent to counter pain and infection and create good healing. It also controls swelling.

— *Hypercal* when applied to the wound, creates fast and healthy healing.

INJURIES *EYE* Only if it is inflamed, then use *Aconite 6* for 3 or 4 days at the rate of 3 doses a day.

— If the eye has pus in it, or an inflamed eye does not respond to Aconite then give *Euphrasia 3* for a few days.

— If there is a great deal of pus present then use *Argentum Nit 6* instead of the Euphrasia — dose as before.

Case History A swan pen had an eye completely hidden by pus. She sat in a corner in a very dejected manner, would not eat or bother with anyone. She was given *Argentum Nit* which completely cleared the eye within a couple of days. Her miserable state changed and she became a happy bird, eager to eat, swim and generally join in with whatever was happening. She was released soon afterwards.

SKIN When a bird is injured by a cat's claws or teeth, or if it is caught on barbed wire, you have a situation of torn flesh and puncture wounds together with danger of infection. There is also pain and shock to deal with.

— The first priority is shock treatment, and *Aconite 200* 3 or 4 doses, ½ hour apart will counter this and reduce pain and inflammation. If any stitching is required it is best done at this stage, of course under anaesthetic. *Hypercal* cream applied to the wounds several times a day, until healed, keeps them clean and aids good healing.

— If there are puncture wounds only and the skin has closed over them, where also the skin is cold give *Ledum 12*, 3 or 4 times a day for a couple of days. This is also a useful remedy against tetanus.

— In puncture wounds with excessive painfulness *Hypericum 30* is the choice, — also for anti-tetanus.

— Sometimes, after stitching, the flesh edges are so febrile they slough off the stitches. Here *Calendula 30* is very useful, dose 3 times a day until improvement.

Case History There was a case of a shelduck who had been caught by rats and the flesh of one wing was practically torn away. The first reaction was to put her down as she was in such a mess. However, she suddenly began flapping strongly, even her badly mutilated wing was getting knocked about. She deserved a chance to live and so she was given *Aconite 200* for a couple of doses and then went into surgery. Under anaesthetic she was stitched up as much as possible, but large holes still remained where the flesh had literally been eaten away. The holes were filled with *Hypercal* cream and *Hypericum 30* was given as soon as she came round and kept up twice a day for a week.

— Not only did the bird live but healed astonishingly well, even new skin filled in the holes. She had no infection and has since accepted a mate and had young.

— A blackbird was caught by a cat and suffered torn flesh, feathers ripped out and a broken wing. He was very shocked and so was given *Aconite 30* for a couple of doses. The wing was set and Aconite continued for two more days. Having established that the wounds were healing, *Symphytum 30* was given

35

for 3 more days, 1 per day. The wounds and the bone healed well.

OPEN WOUNDS All open wounds can be best treated with *Hypercal* tincture or cream. Tincture (dilute 1 drop to 3 drops of cooled boiled water) Cream, just applied from the tube. It does not matter which you choose, which ever best suits the situation. It is a combination of Hypericum and Calendula.

Case History A swan pen was caught up in a fishing line which was wound tightly round her leg, and attached to it was a 3 oz weight. The other end of the line had a hook on it which was embedded in the outside of her neck, which shackled her neck to her leg. The terrified bird was hot and in pain. The line was snipped and a tablet of *Aconite 200* given immediately. The line was removed from her leg and *Hypercal* tincture dripped onto the raw parts. She was lightly sedated and a local anaesthetic applied to the skin round the hook. After its removal *Hypercal* was dripped into the wound. *Hypericum 30* was given to allay infection and soothe pain. Two hours later the bird was walking about, waiting to be let out into an outside area with others.

SLOW HEALING Sometimes wounds are slow to heal in which case *Calendula 30* twice a day for 2 or 3 days should be given.

Case History A moorhen had been tangled in netting and had broken his leg. He was very dazed and his leg was hanging by a muscle, the flesh torn all round the wound. One dose of *Aconite 200* preceded surgery. The bone was aligned and set and the skin flaps stitched up. *Hypercal* was dripped into the wound. In spite of the Hypercal, the wounded flesh was slow to heal. *Calendula 30* was given for three days and all went well. With the splint covering part of the wounds it was not possible to continue the Hypercal in those areas. Afterwards *Symphytum 30* was given to heal the bones. After three weeks the binds were taken off the broken leg, and it was found to have healed beautifully.

GUN SHOT Unfortunately many birds get shot, some are hit but are not killed by organised 'shoots', others are shot 'for fun' by certain types of people from their own gardens or because some birds are considered a nuisance or pests.

— Surgery is nearly always needed here, to remove the penetrated shot and to stitch up the skin. A bird that has been shot in the crop and food is exposed, must have the shot removed before cleaning and stitching because there is a danger of infection if left. The first medication is again *Aconite 30* for 2 or 3 doses then surgery should be carried out. It is good policy to give *Calendula 30* afterwards to aid healthy, fast healing, especially with a crop wound. The bird cannot eat or drink until the wound has healed as the substance would ooze through the wound and cause problems. Injection of Glucose saline is the easy answer here. Keep the bird in the dark or a shady place to encourage sleeping, this puts less strain on the body that cannot take in food. To test the wound for 'leaks' let the bird have a drink of water before it tries food. If the wound is infected give *Hepar Sulph 30* for 3 or 4 doses over a couple of days. You can also dissolve a tablet of Hepar Sulph in a clean tea-spoon with slightly cooled boiled water and drip it onto the infected wound when sufficiently cool. Later follow it with *Hypercal*.

Case History A racing pigeon was shot in his crop, and his food of grain was spilling out. The shot had gone in at the front and out through the side. He was given the treatment as above, Aconite then Calendula. He was a strong bird, and at the end of the second day was able to drink water. The third day he had a good feed, and all was well. He was allowed to go soon after, taking his dissolvable stitches with him.

LEGS Apart from broken legs which we have discussed and paralysis which we will discuss, birds often get stiff legs.

— If the weather is damp and the bird can walk but it is obviously painful to do so, and the right leg is worse, then give *Mag Phos 30*. 2 doses per day over a few days.

— If, however, it is the left that is worse than the right then give *Colocynth 30* instead.

— Sometimes a bird walks on its toes unable to get its foot right down onto the ground, then *Lathyrus 30* should be given.

— Should a foot and leg have swelling and inflammation give *Arsenicum 30* and dose as before.

Case History There was a black-headed gull that had sore legs; he did not want to put any weight on them. He could move them resist a little pressure on them from a hand. He could walk a little but stiffly and it was obviously painful. The right leg seemed worse so I gave him *Mag Phos 30*, which after four doses over two days, had him strutting around and ready to leave.

— A domestic gosling was brought by

39

its distraught owner, who had slipped
trying to catch him, and had fallen with
his hand in the middle of the bird's
back. The gosling's legs were splayed
and he cried out when touched. He lay
in his box for a day with *Arnica 30* being
given every two hours. The following
day he sat more comfortably and was
given *Ruta* to help the strained muscles
and tendons. Two days later he was fine
and returned to his home.

— A moorhen arrived with very dirty
feathers covered in mud. His legs were
sore and inflamed as though he had been
caught by them. They had been trapped.
It was very wet weather and he was
soaked. Water birds sometimes lose
their waterproofing if their feathers have
been allowed to get dirty. When they
preen they cover their plumage with oil
from the preen gland which keeps out
water and also makes them buoyant.
This moorhen had lost his waterproofing and thus was soaked, his sore legs
preventing him from getting out of the
mud. The first treatment was a warm
box under an infra-red lamp and doses
of *Dulcamara 30* three times a day for
two days. The bird started to eat a little
but had fear of water when shown some
to paddle in. He drank but that was all.
He was given *Sulphur 200* once a day for
two days. This is useful if a creature
does not want to wash. He was soon
standing, and with my encouragement

of splashing my hand in the water as though it was washing itself, the moorhen began to copy and have a little bath. He had to have many short bathes and a warm box to prevent him getting a chill until he had preened enough to get his waterproofing back.

LOSS OF APPETITE It is often a mistake to force-feed a bird so I prefer to medicate first. More often than not when a bird is reluctant to eat, its digestion is at fault as well, so food can inflict discomfort or worse. A few doses of *Ignatia 12* twice a day brings back most appetites. A small bird cannot last long without food, so judgement must be used as to how long you can leave a bird without force-feeding.

OILED BIRDS Some birds can be saved with homoeopathy but too many are beyond help, as the digested oil destroys the liver completely. All one can do is try.

— Place the bird in a small, warm box with a low-fitting lid to prevent it from preening. Give *Petroleum 200*, 4 times a day for up to 2 days or until the tar stops showing in its droppings. When the bird is strong enough i.e. eating sprats well, it can be cleaned. It is best to get oiled birds to a cleaning station, as this work is very specialised. The correct strength of washing-up liquid and temperature, rinsing and after-care take a great deal of explanation. Wrong treatment makes it very difficult for the bird to get back its waterproofing. This results in the bird either drowning as it returns to the sea, or dying from exposure on the beach, when it realised it was sinking in the water.

— Assuming you have washed or received a washed bird, the next important step is to counter shock. *Gelsemium 30* for 3 doses, 1 hour apart is good.

— If the bird is lying down for more than a day, give *Psorinium 30* 1 dose a day for 2 days.

— If the bird is weak *Gelsemium 30* again is helpful.

SURGERY To counter shock, prevent bruising and pain, give *Arnica 30* 3 times a day for 2 days.

See also section on Bleeding; Diarrhoea; Loss of Appetite; Fluid Loss; Sleepy; Anaesthetic antidote.

PARALYSIS If the bird is quiet and frail with little movement in the legs or wings (often due to shock or weakness) give *Gelsemium 30* 3 or 4 times a day for up to 2 days.

— If it is trembling, tries to move but falls over because its balance is impaired, use *Argentum Nit 30* and dose as above.

— If the trouble is due to a blow on the lower back give *Arnica 30* as above.

— If the nerves have been injured (leg seems all right but the bird cannot use it) give *Ignatia 200* 1 per day for up to 4 days. If necessary continue dosing but space out once every three days. Stop at 10 doses or drop to 30 potency.

— In other cases that have begun with *Arnica*, where the joints are stiff use *Sulphur 30* twice a day for 3 or 4 days.

— If there is lameness, trembling and twitching of muscles and the feet jerking, use *Zinc Met 6*.

— If the joints are swollen and shiny in appearance: the bird lame with trembling and twitching, use *Manganum Acet 6* twice a day for a few days. Zinc and Mang alternate very well.

Case History A kittiwake arrived with paralysed legs. These birds are not scavengers so it was unlikely to have been poisoned by eating rotten food off rubbish tips. I gave *Sulphur 200* for a couple of doses, then dropped to *Sulphur 30* and alternated with *Rhus Tox 30* for a couple of days. This brought the bird to his feet, enabling him to be released a few days later. I chose Sulphur as the bird was under weight yet was eating, he was also sleepy.

PARASITES Some feather mites are very tiny. They not only cause irritation but if they are not regularly preened away, they multiply rapidly and then inject a poison as they take nourishment from the base of the feathers. Often they can be seen on the heads of birds, known as head-mites. By the time they are obvious the bird is usually weak from their attentions and unless help is at hand, can die. Other types are flying mites, which look like flat-bodied house flies. These are blood suckers and once again can kill their host.

— The treatment firstly is to kill the mites with a bird insect spray. Then give *Ledum 12* — 2 doses morning and evening, or if the case is severe give 4 doses in the day.

— Sometimes water-fowl are infested with leeches, and can attach themselves in the nostrils and even in the mouth of their victim as the bird searches under water for food. It is easy, once in the mouth to get right down the respiratory tract.

— *Panacur* — a non-homoeopathic liquid kills internal parasites. Then treat with Ledum as before.

Case History A black-headed gull arrived in a very weak state, but able to walk about. His wings seemed too heavy to hold up and were dragging on the floor and he kept having to flick them back into position. Inspection revealed his head was covered with head-mites. They looked like small black dots over the crown of his head; as he was in winter dress they were easy to spot as the bird did not have his black cap. He was sprayed with insecticide. (I carefully covered his eyes with my fingers.) He was then given *Lachensis 30* to counter the poison in his blood from the mites, as they continually make wounds in order to suck nourishment.

RESPIRATORY Some respiratory symptoms are to be found under the heading Collapse, so I will just give some suggested medications and leave you to sort out the dosage from the other section and the Case Histories.

— If the bird is hot and has a great deal of fear and laboured breathing, but not wheezing then use *Aconite*.

— If the bird is cold and weak use *Carbo Veg*.

— If the bird is very restless then choose *Arsenicum*. With respiratory problems there is often a relapse and in each case it is no good repeating the same remedy but change to *Sulphur* in each of these instances.

Case Histories A black-headed gull was found being washed by the waves, backwards and forwards on the shore. He was too weak to resist the action. When he arrived sand was caked on his wings as they dragged in the wet sand. He was cold and gasping, lifting his head up and down in the effort to breathe. After two doses of *Carbo Veg 200* 1 hour apart, he stopped his laboured breathing and closed his eyes and tucked his head under his wing for a weary sleep. He awoke several hours later and started gasping again, so I gave him *Sulphur 200* and within five minutes he had stopped, stood up and shook himself. His legs were weak and he did not stay up for long. The following morning he was given *Sulphur 30* and as he was not capable of standing long and seemed to be sore, I gave him *Rhus Tox* in alternation with *Sulphur 30* for a day. The result was that the bird was standing by night fall and did not look back again.

SHOCK This, as I have previously stated, is a killer and so we must act quickly.
— If it is caused by an accident which causes physical injury then *Arnica 200 or 30* is my choice. Depending on the severity, the dosing can be as close as ½

hour and used 2 to 4 times.

— If there is great fear, as from being caught and injured then give *Aconite 200*, as above.

— If the shock is from grief or fright, e.g. a swan witnessing the death of its mate, then *Ignatia 200 or 30*, dose as above.

— If the patient is cold, has no fear, is quiet (apparently tame) sometimes prostrated, the *Gelsemium 30* can work wonders.

SLEEPY There are times when a bird seems absolutely perfect but it cannot stay awake, and will sit on your hand as though it were a tame cage bird. Put its head under its wing and no matter how much you try to disturb it, it just stays like that. Often it is thin, usually due to sleeping instead of finding food.

— If the bird has a warm body then give it *Opium 30*, for 1 or 2 doses ½ hour apart.

— If the body is cold then give *Carbo Veg 200* and dose as before.

You must decide why the bird has got in this state. Look for signs of a bump on the head, missing feathers, injuries under the feathers inflicted by cats' claws and then encourage it to feed. A dose of *Ignatia* will help. The worse thing is if it has been poisoned, perhaps from eating dressed grain from the fields or a poisoned and dying mouse (if it is a bird of prey). If it is one of the latter then you have little chance of saving it.

WINGS Different birds are susceptible to certain types of poisoning and drooping wings are one of the first signs. These heavy limbs are in need of strength to hold them in position.

— Seagulls, in hot weather, scavenge the rubbish tips and are susceptible to food poisoning. *Arsenicum 30* is excellent. 2 to 4 doses 1 to 2 hours apart.

— If the bird is hot and salivating (particularly a herring gull or a great black-backed gull) and maybe gasping then *Ipecacuanha 30* is good ½ to 1 hour apart for 3 or 4 doses.

— If the bird is quiet and cold then *Carbo-Veg 200* should be given, dose 2 or 3 doses 1 hour apart.

— If the bird improves but is still weak then turn to the section on paralysis for further treatment.

— If you have found a thin pigeon in the fields then give *Aurum 30* to try to counter possible mercury poisoning.

— If the bird cannot stand or is wobbly use *Merc Sol 30*.

— If poisoned meat is suspected *Pyrogen 30* is also very good, especially if the droppings are very offensive and dark.

TUMOURS Sometimes budgerigars get this problem and it is not always easy to operate.

— If they are fatty cysts use *Calc carb 30* twice a day for 2 days then once a day for a week, then once a week till there is improvement.

— If the cyst is hard then give *Silica 30* dose as above.

— If the lump is hard with weight loss which suggests cancer then try *Scirrhinum 200* 1 dose weekly.

As you will see from the case histories, it is not always the obvious that cures. I can only give a general guide in treatment. If your chosen treatment from this guide fails, do not despair for with help from the Materia Medica, which follows, and possibly a little more detective work on why the bird is ill, you could find another remedy. Like some of my case histories it is not always the first diagnosis that is the answer.

Always remember symptoms are caused by something, as is the body's reaction to it. It is the cause which is important in finding the remedy and, unfortunately, our little feathered friends are not very good at telling us what has happened. We do, however, develop an intuition for this detective work, or perhaps an enlightened guess.

BIRD MATERIA MEDICA

ACETIC ACID — (glacial)

Antidote to vapour anaesthetics.

It can liquefy severe catarrh which is causing desperate gasping for breath.

As it also antidotes Aconite, Ignatia and Opium. Acetic acid itself, must be antidoted before further use of other medications. Aconite, actually antidotes it, so one dose of this and then continue. Acetic acid is not compatible with Arnica, Lachesis, Mercuris and Causticum, so care must be taken to antidote it first.

ACONITUM NAPELLUS (Monkshood) — Aconite

For effects of shock from injury, where there is fear; physical and mental restlessness. First aid for skin injuries from cat scratches and tears; inflammations. Diarrhoea during very hot weather.

Where there is redness of skin and the bird is very restless and frightened. State of collapse, where heat and fear are present.

Duration of action 14— 40 days.

ALUMEN (Common Potash Alum) — Alum

Useful in cases of Diarrhoea, especially where bird is eating well and it will not cease or is slow to go.

It antidotes lead poisoning and other mercurials.

APIS MELLIFICA (Honey bee) — Apis

In most cases of swellings, especially those sustained from bee stings. Skin sensitive to touch, hot and swollen. Use also in cases where eyes are red with swollen surrounds.

ARGENTUM NITRICUM (Nitrate of Silver) — Argentum Nit.

Where there is loss of balance, and co-ordination of mind and body. Where there is trembling in affected parts. Legs that are withered; bird agitated. Eye ulcers and abundant discharge.

Duration of action 30 days.

ARNICA (Leopard's Bane) — Arnica

First aid for any injuries from blows; where there is bruising or danger of concussion. Use for concussion. Sprains or strains respond to this remedy. Useful before and after surgery. On broken skin with bruising, never apply physically to the wound, but use internally. It can, however, be used as an ointment to bruises if skin is intact. Cases of diarrhoea (even bloody) caused by accident, or shock from surgery, respond to this. Can be used for problems resulting from old injuries (in humans, even 20-year-old cases had responded that had not been treated with Arnica at the time).

Aconite is complimentary.

Duration of action 6— 10 days.

ARSENICUM ALBUM (Arsenic Trioxide) — Arsenicum

Bird is restless and prepared to give a good peck. Body temperature is normal to touch and it has bright eyes.

Useful in cases of food poisoning, often caused by bad meat; usually green-stained vent feathers are obvious.

For red, swollen legs, but not as puffy as for Apis.

Gradual loss of weight from impaired nutrition.

Ill effects from fright.

Paralysis with atrophy of legs.

Putrid odour from discharges.

Ailments during varying weather conditions.

Duration of action 60— 90 days.

AURUM METALLUM (Gold) — Aurum

Cases where the bird is quiet and ready to give up and die. It may give a half-hearted peck, as though to say, 'Go away and leave me alone'. Sometimes it is glassy-eyed.

Knees weak, worse in cold weather; usually a remedy for winter weather complaints.

Antidotes lead poisoning.

Duration 50— 60 days.

BELLADONNA (Deadly Nightshade) — Belladonna

Bird is restless, unnaturally glaring eyes; convulsive movements; aversion to water; changeable attitudes. It attacks one moment and hides away the next.

Useful for swollen joints; tottering gait.

Cold legs and feet with jerking limbs.

Wants to stand up and will not lie down.

Duration of action 1— 7 days.

BELLIS PERENNIS (Daisy) — Bellis

Use for results of accidents where there are nerve injuries. Where there is lameness from sprains or strains; sore joints and muscular stiffness.

First remedy in injuries to deeper tissues, after major surgery work.

CALCAREA CARBONICA OSTREARUM
(Carbonate of Lime) — Calc. carb.

Useful for abscesses in deep muscles.

For relapses during convalescence.

It helps blood to clot.

Eyes sensitive to light, bird hides its head in a corner. Eye-lids swollen.

Extreme difficulty in breathing.

Duration of action 60 days.

CALCAREA SUPHURICA (Plaster of Paris) — Calc. Sulph.

This follows Ruta well in cases of stiffness of legs.

Useful where there is inflammation with discharge of thick yellow matter.

Diarrhoea with blood.

CALENDULA OFFICINALIS (Marigold) — Calendula

A great healer of wounds. It stops bleeding and aids formation of healthy tissue. Can be applied locally as a tincture or cream or taken internally in tablet form.

Useful for lacerated scalp wounds.

CARBO VEGETABILIS (Vegetable Charcoal) — Carbo veg.

The bird is usually slow, quiet and cold. Eyes partly closed, 'doesn't care any more'. This remedy has been termed the 'corpse reviver' when used in high potencies.

Use for cases of food poisoning due to fish.

Duration of action 60 days.

DULCAMARA (Bittersweet) — Dulc.

Ailments that are caused by damp. Recurrent rheumatism during wet weather.

Birds, that look ill but no cause can be found, and it is cold and wet weather, often will respond to this remedy.

Stiff legs; drooping wings, all signs of weakness; chills; but during wet weather.

EUPHRASIA (Eyebright) — Euphrasis

Use for running eyes; red, sore eyes. Where there is free discharging of matter from them.

GELSEMIUM — (Yellow Jasmine) — Gels.

Tiredness is the great sign. Where there is weakness or paralysis.

The bird shows no fear of handling; is fatigued after the slightest movement.

Bad effects from fear or fright.

Where there is chilliness.

Duration of action 30 days.

HAMAMELIS VIRGINICA (Witch Hazel) — Hamamelis

It stops bleeding.

Is ideal after operations and supersedes the use of morphia.

It is of great value in open, painful wounds.

Bruised soreness of affected parts.

HEPAR SULPHURIS CALCAREUM (Hahnemann's Calcium Sulphide) — Hepar Sulph.

Use where there is suppuration with pain; unhealthy skin; every little injury suppurates.

Ulcers that are very sensitive.

Abscesses that bleed easily.

Duration of action 40— 50 days.

HYPERCAL — mixture of Hypericum and Calendula

Use for wounds. Cleansing, healing and pain removing.

HYPERICUM (St. John's Wort) — Hypericum

Useful for injuries involving nerves, especially to toes and claws.

Injured nerves after predator attacks.

Relieves pain after surgery.

Paralysed legs due to mechanical injury to spinal cord. (Higher potencies only of use here.)

IGNATIA (St. Ignatius' Bean) — Ignatia

For effects of grief and loss of mate, and fear.

Very nervous birds; ideal for females that are quick, but submissive.

Rapid change of characteristics from quiet to panic; also in ailments where the bird at one moment seems fine, and the next is ill, then better again.

Useful in injuries of the spine.

IPECACUANHA (Ipecac root) — Ipec.

For upset stomachs, where bird is hot and often salivating.

Where there is respiratory trouble, rattling of mucus in the chest or the throat and gasping for breath.

Eyes are often partly closed with weakness in body.

Duration of action 7— 10 days.

LACHESES (Bushmaster) — Lachesis

Where wounds have dirt in them and become infected.

Where there is a septic state; danger of gangrene.

Dark appearance of wounds.

Duration of action 30— 40 days.

LATHYRUS (Chick pea) — Lath.

Useful where there is paralysis without pain. Legs dangle when bird is picked up.

For slow recovery of nerve power.

Sleepy patient; cold limbs.

Cannot lift feet clear of the ground yet cannot lower heels to the ground.

LEDUM (Marsh tea) — Ledum

Use for puncture wounds; useful as an anti-tetanus. Especially indicated where the wound is cold.

Soles of feet painful; can hardly step on them.

Duration of action 30 days.

LYCOPODIUM (Club Moss) — Lycopodium

Ailments that develop slowly, functional powers weakening with failure of digestive powers, where liver is seriously disturbed. (Can be useful for oiled birds that show oil in their droppings.)

Duration of action 40— 50 days.

MANGANUM ACETICUM (Manganese Acetate) — Mang.

For progressive paralysis with wasting of limbs.

Where there is feeble and staggering gait; leans forward in walking so falls onto beak.

Swelling of joints; sore feet.

Worse in cold weather.

MERCURIUS HYDRARGYRUM (Quick-silver) — Merc.

Indicated in loss of weight; where there is feather loss; tremors, great prostration; sensitive to heat — cold breath.

Ulceration of mouth and throat; abscesses; excretions smell foul; tendency to pus formation, which is greenish, thin and streaked with blood.

Antidote to mercury poisoning.

Duration of action 1— 3 days.

NATRUM MURIATUM (Chloride of Sodium) — Nat Mur.

Indicated where there is weakness and weariness.

Ill effects of fright.

Easily irritable.

Complements Ignatia.

OPIUM-PAPAVER SOMNIFERUM (Dried latex of poppy) — Opium

Where there is drowsy stupor. Painlessness. Lack of reaction to stimuli. Warm to hot bodied.

Patient does not react to indicated remedies.

Birds usually tuck their heads under their wings and refuse to wake up; sometimes (if small enough) sit on your hand without fear and look dazed.

Duration of action 7 days.

OXALICUM ACIDUM (Sorrel acid) — Oxalic acid

For short jerky breathing. Where there is constriction.

Paralysis due to spinal injury.

PETROLEUM (Crude rock-oil) — Petrol

Antidotes oil pollution, especially indicated in oiled birds that have digested crude oil off their feathers.

Duration of action 40— 50 days.

PLUMBUM METALLICUM (Lead) — Plumbum

Where there is lead poisoning, especially in paralysis of wings.

Progressive muscular atrophy, excessive and rapid emaciation.

Lack of red blood corpuscles.

Do not give many doses of this remedy.

Duration of action 20— 30 days.

PHOSPHORICUM ACIDUM (Phosphoric acid) — Phos Ac.

Loss of vital fluids, after diarrhoea or blood loss.

Where there is listlessness.

Effects of shock; gives up struggle of existence.

Difficult breathing.

Duration of action 40 days.

PSORINUM (Scabies Vesicle) — Psorinum

Where bird is cold, and there is a lack of reaction to well-chosen remedies.

Secretions have a filthy smell.

A single dose of 30 or 200 is usually sufficient; follow by the indicated remedy once more.

Duration of action 30— 40 days.

PULSATILLA (Wind flower) — Puls.

It is usually indicated in a gentle female, who is changeable in characteristics. They are better outside; have little or no thirst and are worse from heat.

Limbs are painful; stiffness of legs, swollen veins in wings. Feet are red, inflamed and swollen.

Bird wants to sit down. It is better, however, if it will walk about outside.

Duration of action 40 days.

PYROGENIUM (Artificial Sepsin) — Pyrogen.

In cases of food poisoning where there is offensive brown-black diarrhoea.

It is a great antiseptic.

Discharges are always offensive; there is pain and burning in affected parts.

Patient is restless.

RHUS TOXICODENDRON (Poison ivy) — Rhus Tox.

Rheumatic pains are worse when limbs are kept still (bird will be stiff until it gets moving).

Ailments from strains; getting wet while hot.

Rheumatism in cold season.

Limbs stiff, paralysed; hot painful swelling of joints; hates cold air.

Duration of action 1— 7 days.

RUTA GRAVEOLENS (Rue bitterwort) — Ruta

For strained limbs; usually after Arnica has stopped working.

Ideal for stiff legs and/or wings.

Duration of action 30 days.

SILICEA (Silica pure flint) — Silica

Promotes suppuration, so ripens abscesses.

Bird is cold and tired, yet excitable.

Slow recovery after respiratory troubles.

Loss of power in legs; soles of feet sore.

Duration of action 40— 60 days.

SCIRRHINUM

A specific for cancer. To be used with care. Dose only as indicated.

SULPHUR (Sublimated Sulphur) — Sulphur

Where dirty-feathered birds are afraid to go into water having lost the water-proofing of their plumage.

Useful as an intercurrent with Aconite in cases of collapse when Aconite is indicated.

Also as an intercurrent with Ipec. in cases of collapse.

Complaints that relapse.

Birds that are lazy but snappy; thin and weak, but have a good appetite.

Helps in cases of paralysed legs after use of Rhus tox.

Birds are hot bodied.

Duration of action 40— 60 days.

SYMPHYTUM (Comfrey — Knitbone) — Symphytum

For good healing of broken bones, tendons and sinews. Increases strength of healing and speeds up time.

Helps with injured eyes.

URTICA URENS (Stinging nettle) — Urtica Urens

For burns and scalds.

Can be used in tincture, cream or tablets.

ZINCUM METALLICUM (Zinc) — Zinc

Lameness and weakness with twitching of various muscles.

Sensitive to noise; lethargic; has cold feet.

Works well with Mang.

Duration of action 30— 40 days.